Trees

by Aiden Mark
illustrated by Julie Knoblock

Harcourt
SCHOOL PUBLISHERS

Requests for permission to make copies of any part of the work should be addressed to School Permissions and Copyrights, Harcourt, Inc., 6277 Sea Harbor Drive, Orlando, Florida 32887–6777. Fax: 407-345-2418.

HARCOURT and the Harcourt Logo are trademarks of Harcourt, Inc., registered in the United States of America and/or other jurisdictions.

Printed in the United States of America

ISBN 10: 0-15-351254-7
ISBN 13: 978-0-15-351254-4

Ordering Options
ISBN 10: 0-15-351211-3 (Grade 1 Advanced Collection)
ISBN 13: 978-0-15-351211-7 (Grade 1 Advanced Collection)
ISBN 10: 0-15-358022-4 (package of 5)
ISBN 13: 978-0-15-358022-2 (package of 5)

1 2 3 4 5 6 7 8 9 10   179   15 14 13 12 11 10 09 08 07 06

Trees can't run or do a jig.
Trees can grow to be very big.

Add sun and water,
and trees will grow.
Up and up and up they go.

Trees can be thick.
Trees can be tall.
Trees can be thin.
Trees can be small.

This tree has
some lumps and bumps.
This tree now is just a stump.

Some trees grow food
like these red plums.
You can eat them.
Oh, yum, yum!

Look in here, and you will see.
Many birds live in this tree.

A tree can't run,
but it does grow.
Up and up and up it goes!